The
Executor's
Roadmap

The Executor's Roadmap

Published by
American Institute for Economic Research
250 Division Street, P.O. Box 1000
Great Barrington, Mass. 01230
Phone: (888)528-1216
Email: info@aier.org
Website: www.aier.org

Book design by Jane McWhorter

ISBN: 978-0-913610-09-1

ABOUT SMART DECISIONS

This book, as others in the *Smart Decisions* series, is designed to help you take some necessary steps to improve your personal financial life. Each book is meticulously researched to give you as complete a guide as possible.

It may very well be that a short accessible *Smart Decisions* handbook will be all you'll need to meet a challenge or get started in a direction you'd like to go. But like a good friend, no title in the series claims to be the only source of wisdom on a particular topic. A critical component to each publication in the series is a list of resources that can help further expand your knowledge.

There's a reason for this. The American Institute for Economic Research is not a commercial book publisher. It is a non-profit institute with education as part of its core mission. We succeed when you know more.

AIER pursues its mission through many avenues: seminars, issue briefs, business-cycle analysis, and working papers as well as books. The Institute has been helping people in this way since its inception during the Great Depression. You can access much of our research at our website **www.aier.org**. Web-based worksheets and other tools directly related to this *Smart Decisions* publication, as well as other AIER books, are available at **www.aier.org/bookstore**. Or you can call 888-528-1216.

Two books may be of particular interest to readers of *The Executor's Roadmap. How to Avoid Financial Tangles* gives more detailed information about ownership, trusts, and other issues pertinent to estates. *If Something Should Happen* outlines the basics of estate planning and provides help assembling critical information where loved ones can easily find it.

Whatever your circumstance, whether you are starting out your financial life, a longtime investor keeping on top of your game or somewhere in between, we welcome you to *Smart Decisions* and to AIER.

Marcia Stamell
Creative director and editor
The American Institute for Economic Research
Great Barrington, Massachusetts

Contents

The Executor's Roadmap

By Jennifer Keeney-Bleeg

AIER • AMERICAN INSTITUTE for ECONOMIC RESEARCH

Great Barrington, MA

HOW DO YOU LEARN HOW TO BE AN EXECUTOR?

At the beginning of my research for this book, I asked this question of a number of people who had settled their loved ones' estates. Invariably, they sighed and said their best training came from plunging in and making mistakes along the way. Once they completed the job, they felt they could capably do it again. Of course, not many of us need to, or—let's admit it—would want to serve as an executor more than once.

In this book, we wanted to make it easier for you to understand the basics of the role from the start. Our goal was to explain in plain terms what tasks you need to accomplish, what challenges might lay ahead, and how and when to lean on professionals for help in an effort to avoid mistakes. Along the way, I consulted a number of experts with my own questions. I'm especially grateful to attorneys Elizabeth Garlovsky, Jeffrey Greathouse, and Jeffrey Katz for their help at the early stages of this book's research.

— Jennifer Keeney-Bleeg

1 • How this book can guide you

If you're an executor now, or someone has chosen you to serve as an executor sometime in the future, this book is your roadmap.

It distills the work of an executor into the essentials. That may be all you have the patience, time, or emotional energy to absorb after a death—especially if the person you lost was a spouse, parent, or someone else close to you. If you need to start settling an estate now, this book will frame out the basic tasks you'll need to handle in the months ahead, whether you have a will to guide you or not. If you're fortunate to know well in advance that you'll be the executor of an estate, this book can help you make the most of your preparation time. There are steps you can take now to smooth things out later for the good of the estate and its beneficiaries.

The executor is the person responsible for carrying out the final wishes of the deceased and managing the estate's financial obligations. In the weeks and months after the death, you'll inform various parties of the death, work with other beneficiaries and hired advisers, and catalog and secure the decedent's assets—everything from life insurance and real estate to antiques hidden in the attic. You'll pay debts and taxes using estate assets, and distribute what remains to beneficiaries.

It is your duty to work fairly and honestly with those who will inherit the decedent's property. At times, depending on the complexity of the estate and the number of other beneficiaries involved, you may feel you're part business manager, part psychologist, and part diplomat.

This book outlines the key concepts you need to know in the general order you need to know them. But it is also designed so that you can dip into chapters on an as-needed basis. You may need to review probate (Chapter 13), for example, in order to know how much you will need a lawyer's counsel (Chapter 22). And as you take inventory of assets and liabilities (Chapter 11), you'll probably need to understand various types of ownership (Chapter 12) and how accountants and appraisers may assist you (Chapter 23). So feel free to skip around based on your needs.

2 • Accepting the role

Serving as an executor—or similarly, the successor trustee of a trust—is a mixed blessing. On the positive side, you have the opportunity to give the decedent a final gift by taking care of the estate in the manner he or she would have liked. That can be an honor and also help in the process of grieving.

The role may also test your patience and consume many hours of your time, especially if the decedent's state of residence has complicated estate laws, or if you have several incompatible beneficiaries to manage. There is no rule determining how long the process will take. While some estates can be settled in as little as six months, it is more common for settlement to take 12 to 18 months. Depending on the complexity of the estate and where you live in relation to the decedent, you may need to take time away from work (or certainly devote a substantial amount of your spare time) to settle the estate.

You are entitled to request compensation for your efforts. Many executors decline payment because it counts as taxable income, and if they are also beneficiaries of the estate, they stand to inherit anyway. If you would like to request payment and the will does not dictate how much you are entitled to receive, search for your state's probate code online and look for information on "executor compensation" or "personal representative compensation." Some state laws provide direction about how to calculate compensation, while others (less helpfully) indicate that the executor is entitled to "reasonable compensation," in which case you must determine what costs are reasonable to charge for your administration of the estate.

Even if you feel duty-bound to accept the role, particularly if you are the spouse or adult child of the decedent, you are not legally bound to do so. You may feel the task is too burdensome based on your time limitations or your relationships with beneficiaries. If the person who selected you is still living, you have some time to decide whether or not to accept the responsibility, though it's best to give him or her time to choose another executor. Even if the person who selected you has already died, you may decline. The job will either go to an alternate executor, if the will names one, or to a person appointed by the probate court. If you have been appointed executor by the probate court and decide to resign, you will have to inform the court and provide a written account of any tasks you completed to settle the estate.

Accepting the job will be much easier if you have the opportunity to work with the person who selected you. If you don't have that chance, bear in mind that many adults feel unprepared to serve as executors. You'll do fine if you're organized, conscientious, adept at communicating with others, and committed to doing your best for the estate.

If you need to start settling an estate now, skip ahead to Chapter 4 for next steps. If the person who named you executor is still living, keep reading. Now is a good time for you both to talk about the estate plan. A poor estate plan makes it more challenging to settle the estate and to ensure that it is settled in accordance with the decedent's wishes.

3 • Plan in advance

The best time to gather critical information about an estate is when the person who has named you executor is still living. If given that chance, have a conversation. Ideally, it should cover more than where to find documents, who the heirs are, and how to access financial accounts and password-protected computer accounts.

Talk through the estate plan together. (See "Elements of an Estate Plan" in the Appendix for a list of items to cover.) Even if you don't get clear guidance on everything you discuss, gathering as much information as possible will put you ahead of the game.

Air the dirty laundry now. Does the will include or exclude anyone intentionally or unintentionally? Does it mention assets that are no longer part of the estate? Does it include a valued asset, like a family summer home, that will spark conflict if heirs disapprove of plans for the transfer of that asset? If there is a business in the estate, is there a clear exit strategy that will preserve its value for heirs? Is there property located in separate states or countries? If you don't address these issues now, you may encounter hurdles down the line.

If the person has minor children, discuss who should raise them and serve as guardian of assets they inherit should the other parent also die. While this is not an easy topic to consider, having clear wishes outlined in advance—and ensuring that preferred guardian(s) have carefully considered their roles—can help limit discord later. Similarly, while adult children will not have a guardian appointed, they may have a trustee of their assets until they reach a specified age, say 25 or 30.

Suggest a joint meeting with an estate attorney to discuss, at least in broad terms, how to prevent as many assets as possible from going through probate court. (Learn more about probate court in Chapter 13.) Remember, the probate system was designed to protect creditors, not beneficiaries. The attorney, an accountant, or a financial planner can also help you assess the estate's likelihood of owing estate tax and recommend strategies to avoid or minimize it.

Encourage the person who has named you executor to pay off debts and settle conflicts so you don't inherit them. Ask for written directions to guide you through any complex matters that the estate may present, like a bankruptcy or pending lawsuit, for instance. Find out who, if anyone, has power of attorney for end-of-life financial and health matters. If you are to be granted power of attorney or appointed health care proxy, get final wishes in writing to eliminate guesswork and family disagreement.

It can help you avoid conflicts after the death if those inheriting from the estate know about the estate plan in advance. The best way to do this is for the person who chose you as executor to meet with you and all other beneficiaries to discuss future plans for distributing the property and how you, as executor, will be involved. A group meeting ensures everyone hears the same message and has an opportunity to listen to each other's concerns, but you and the person who chose you as executor can meet with everyone individually if gathering as a group isn't possible. The topics you discuss should align with the legally binding will or trust document.

Finally, for the sake of simplicity and the estate's pocketbook, it's best for an estate to have one executor. If there are two or more of you, most decisions will require your joint consent and, in many cases, your joint signature. That's a logistical challenge if you live far apart and a personal challenge when you disagree. If possible, ask the person who selected you as a co-executor to choose one person as executor and another person as an alternate.

4 • Communicate with transparency

After the death occurs, you will need to communicate with beneficiaries and other interested parties. The executor or the estate attorney must notify the beneficiaries of the estate and, in many states, people who were disinherited so they have an opportunity to contest the will. But that is just a first step.

Even if you are managing amicable beneficiaries and there are no disinherited people in the mix, keeping in touch with heirs is the most important rule for an executor to remember. Tell beneficiaries when you will need to file paperwork with the probate court, if and how you plan to consult outside professionals, how you're handling the sale of assets, and when you will be able to distribute estate proceeds.

One strategy is to update everyone regularly via monthly e-mails. Mention tasks you have completed and those you plan to complete in the next few weeks. Include information in three key categories: payment of debts, legal and tax filings, and status of assets (inventory, appraisals, purchases, sales, and distributions). Don't withhold details. A beneficiary who believes you are concealing information or mismanaging the estate can challenge you in probate court.

Your open dialogue with beneficiaries can also help you focus your efforts appropriately. For example, do the beneficiaries support renovating the decedent's vacation home to fetch a better price for it? Or do they want to sell the property as soon as possible, knowing they will have to accept less for it? Knowing their desired outcomes can help you make better decisions for the estate.

If you will be a co-executor of the estate, establish guidelines at the outset to communicate at regular intervals with the other co-executor(s). For most estates in this situation, it will make sense to divide tasks and convene for the signing of documents when needed (or agree to a lot of FedEx-ing back and forth). If you don't see this division of labor working, one co-executor may step down at the beginning if he or she trusts the other to make decisions on the estate's behalf. You might also pay an estate attorney or other adviser to serve as a mediator, though you and your co-executor are still jointly responsible for hiring people to manage the estate, for overseeing its gains or losses in value, and for the final settlement.

5 • Immediately after the death

The first hours and days following a death can be an emotional blur as you consider your loss and your responsibility to the decedent. If you are a close relative of the decedent, you will not only be experiencing the emotional loss. You will also likely have a role in the immediate aftermath of the death, though your role as executor has not yet begun.

First, a doctor, hospice nurse, or coroner will make the cause of death pronouncement so a death certificate can be prepared. If the death occurred in a nursing home or hospital, talk to the staff about how long you and other relatives who wish to stay with the decedent may do so. The staff should be able to arrange for the transfer of the body to a funeral home and advise you of when you will need to remove personal belongings from their facility. Timing is less of an issue if the decedent died at home, but the family will need to arrange for the transfer of the body themselves.

As a relative of the decedent, you'll share the news with family and friends, as well as with regular visitors who had been providing health services or meals. You might also need to contact a funeral director or member of the clergy to plan for a funeral or memorial. This person can help you publish the brief death notice that appears in the newspaper (your probate court may require it) and possibly a longer-form obituary about the decedent's life.

While your formal appointment as executor will likely not happen until after the funeral, you can take some steps to care for the decedent's property in the meantime. Find the will, confirm you are named as executor, and store the document in a safe place. (If there is no will, look to Chapter 8 for guidance.) Protect any vacant real estate the decedent owned. If the decedent had been living at home, arrange for the long-term care of pets left behind, stop mail delivery, hire a service to mow the lawn, clear items from the refrigerator, and use timers on lights to make the property appear occupied. If the decedent left vehicles or boats that were not owned jointly with someone else, store them (and their keys) in a safe location until they can be transferred to new owners.

Lock up any additional valuables. You'll want to protect them from break-ins, visitors to the home, or even well-meaning beneficiaries who might want to claim keepsakes before they can be distributed according to the decedent's wishes.

If the decedent had been living in a rented property, check the lease and state law for direction on next steps. If the decedent had a month-to-month rental at the time of death, you'll need to clear the property by the end of the month (or, in some states, give as many as 30 days' notice) to end the estate's obligation to pay rent. If the decedent had signed a long-term lease, the estate is liable for paying rent throughout the lease term. However, the estate can stop paying rent if the landlord finds a new tenant before the lease expires.

Request multiple certified copies of the decedent's death certificate. The funeral director or county vital records office can provide copies for a charge. You will likely need one to transfer each major asset, one to access the person's safe deposit box, one to collect insurance benefits, and so on. Get 10 to 15 copies to handle your needs following the funeral. You can order extras if you need them.

6 • First steps as executor

As you prepare to take on the role of executor, the most important document you will need to have on hand is the decedent's will. It is the blueprint you will use to determine how to settle the estate. Even if there is also a trust that's part of the estate, the will provides the framework dictating how the trust money will be used and how long the trust will last.

Make copies of the will and file the original with the probate court. (For more information about navigating probate court, see Chapter 13.) Many states require that you do this within as little as 10 days to a month of the death, so make sure you check the court's website and comply with its timeline. The court will issue you a document called Letters Testamentary, or something similar, which authorizes you to begin your duties as executor. This entitles you to open and close bank accounts, pay taxes, and manage assets for the estate. The court will also issue an order to officially open the probate case.

Once you are officially named executor, you'll need to take steps beyond immediate concerns such as protecting property or caring for pets. You'll have to notify a number of organizations about the death. Contact organizations that had been providing income or other services—like the Social Security Administration, credit card companies, insurers, banks, and government agencies providing benefits, for example. Cancel utilities that are no longer needed for a vacant property but retain key services like electricity, water, and gas until the property is transferred to a new owner.

You will want to cancel print or online publication subscription accounts that might have automatic renewals in place. Remember, many digital services bill monthly; you will want to cancel this type of account as well. In addition, there may be social media accounts you want to close or set to memorial status. (For more information on working with online accounts, see Chapter 10.)

The estate will need its own bank account, which you will use to pay the decedent's final bills and other expenses. To open the account, you'll need to acquire a taxpayer ID for the estate from the IRS. The IRS refers to the estate's tax ID number as an employer identification number, or EIN. Visit the IRS website and search for "How to Apply for an EIN." These application instructions apply to everyone, not just estate executors. You will find instructions for applying online, or via phone, fax, or mail. If you have any questions, call the IRS at 800-829-1040 for assistance.

Opening a basic checking account will suffice for most estates. Set one up in the state where the decedent lived—if you live in another state and open the account at your local bank, you may have to file an additional tax return if the account accrues income. (Note: If the estate includes a trust and you're the successor trustee, there may already be an account in place for you to use. See Chapter 14 for more information.)

Once you have an estate bank account in place, transfer all funds from the decedent's bank account and close that account. To avoid bank charges, just make sure you have first canceled any automatic payments scheduled to be paid from the decedent's personal account.

7 • Legal terminology 101

When you study the will, you may encounter legal language that will influence the way the estate is distributed. The terms *per capita* and *per stirpes*, for example, can have vastly different implications on who inherits how much. Per capita distribution means each heir, children and grandchildren alike, gets an equal share. Per stirpes distribution refers to when children inherit the share intended for a parent who died before he or she could inherit.

You may also find a number of terms in the will that affect your actions. An *executor's bond* is an insurance policy the probate court may require (and which the will may excuse you from having to purchase) to protect heirs from any losses to the estate that are caused by the executor. *Devise* is real estate (also termed *real property*) an heir inherits upon the death of the decedent. *Residue* is all property not specifically mentioned in the will that will nonetheless be distributed to a beneficiary. *Issue* are a decedent's children and grandchildren—direct descendants as opposed to spouses, siblings, and cousins.

Most executors have to consult professionals—attorneys most typically. This means you aren't expected to answer all the questions about an estate on your own. But it greatly helps to take note of terms you don't know so that you interpret the will correctly.

8 • When there is no will

If you do not have a will (or have an incomplete will) to guide you—and probate court named you executor in accordance with state law—you're not alone. Most Americans die without leaving a will. While this leaves you without key information about how the decedent wanted his or her property distributed, you can still settle the estate. In essence, you'll follow many of the same steps outlined in this book for executors named in a will: You'll take an inventory, work with the probate court, pay debts, and disburse assets to the heirs.

You may find the estate contains assets that pass to heirs outside the confines of the will because they designate a beneficiary or co-owner who automatically inherits the asset. These include jointly held real estate, items held in a trust, life insurance proceeds, retirement plans, and payable-on-death bank accounts. When you sort through the decedent's belongings, you may find documents that name the beneficiary or co-owner of such assets.

For other assets, such as solely owned real estate or personal property, you'll have to look to state law—intestate succession law, specifically—for direction on who inherits. (Find laws pertaining to your state at **www.statelocalgov.net.**) In most cases, the only people who can inherit under intestate succession law are spouses, registered domestic partners, and blood relatives. How the estate is to be divided among those heirs differs by state. Before you distribute any assets, make sure you know who is eligible to inherit (the children of a deceased heir, for example, might be able to claim their parent's share in some states).

9 • Create a file system

Whether you store the decedent's files electronically or prefer the folders of a file box, you'll need a system that organizes records for easy reference. Well-maintained records will help you update beneficiaries regularly and anticipate conflicts before they escalate. And, if the estate loses any value before it's settled, your records will help prove it was not due to your negligence.

Store documents from the decedent, such as the will, trust, and account statements, as well as detailed records of every task you handle for the estate. Keep records of debts you pay and assets you sell or distribute. Save copies of documents you file with the probate court. Also include correspondence you have with beneficiaries, creditors, and estate professionals.

The complexity of the file system will reflect the complexity of the estate as well as your own organizational preferences. Below are some file categories you may find helpful.

Appraisals	Probate court
Bank accounts	Real estate
Bills (paid and unpaid)	Retirement accounts
Correspondence	Social Security
Death certificates	Stocks
Deeds	Tax returns
Employment	Titles (to vehicles, boats, etc.)
Inventory of assets and debts	Trust
Insurance (life and property)	Will
Medical expenses	

10 • Assemble critical information

Like many executors, you may have to comb through a tangle of documents to pin down elements of the estate you're trying to settle. Even the best-organized estates can be daunting.

It helps to make a list of what you need to find and read. Important papers include the will, trust (if applicable), life insurance policies, and tax returns. Look also for any paperwork that documents what the person owned. This includes property deeds, automobile registration papers, and bank statements. If the decedent owned a business, you may find paperwork detailing the succession agreement. If there is a will, develop a complete list of beneficiaries named in it, along with their birthdates, Social Security numbers, mailing addresses, email addresses, and phone numbers.

To locate what you need, you may have to find the key to the decedent's home office filing cabinet, or, since many people receive account statements electronically (and manage a host of other tasks online), retrieve online passwords. If you're lucky, you'll find a list of relevant usernames and passwords. If not, you may be able to secure permission to access various accounts by presenting the documentation that named you executor. While it can be a challenge for an executor to access this information, many states are beginning to enact digital property laws that help executors locate what they need.

To trace the estate's digital footprint, start by connecting to the person's e-mail account. Now that you have Letters Testamentary in hand, the decedent's Internet provider may grant you access. The same goes for other companies through which the decedent held online accounts. Look for bank, investment, and mortgage company accounts.

Besides learning what the estate owns, you need to find out what the estate owes. Search for credit card records, mortgages, and car or home equity loans. There may be unpaid funeral and medical expenses. Remember also that before the estate can be settled, it may incur probate and legal fees and owe taxes. You don't have to pay these expenses now; just begin to learn what the estate may owe.

Getting a complete picture of the estate may require access to the decedent's safe deposit box. State laws vary widely here. If you are not listed as an authorized user but are an immediate family member, you may be able to access the box in the presence of a bank employee in order to locate the will. If you are not immediate family and the bank will not grant you access, the probate court can authorize your access as executor for the purpose of locating the will.

As you gather information, ask yourself some critical questions. Will you have to sell complicated investments or keep a family business running? Does the will mention the heirs who should inherit specific assets? Have any marriages, divorces, or births (that affect the heirs) happened in the family since the will was drafted? Are there children not mentioned in the will who will feel entitled to estate property? The answers to these questions will give you a sense of any complications you will have to address as part of the estate's settlement—and how you will need to communicate with beneficiaries and consult professionals as a result.

11 • Make a written inventory

Taking inventory of the decedent's assets and liabilities will help you determine the estate's value. This serves several purposes.

First, you'll need to provide the probate court with the fair market value of each estate asset if the estate needs to pass through probate. (If the estate is small enough, it might qualify for simplified probate, which makes it easier to transfer property, or it may not need to pass through probate at all. The rules vary from state to state, so you'll need to check with your state's probate court website. For more information on probate, see Chapter 13.)

Your clear valuation of the estate also can help streamline discussions with members of your estate settlement team. At a glance, the professionals you consult will be able to determine if the estate is likely to owe federal or state estate tax, for example, or if you might need to purchase more insurance on estate property.

Finally, a reliable valuation will help you see what each beneficiary will inherit so you can divide those assets as the decedent intended.

Start with the estate's assets. List every kind of asset the decedent owned—real estate, checking account, family business, individual retirement account, life insurance policy, antique car, etc.—along with its fair market value as of the date the decedent passed away.

Calculating asset values will require some legwork. You'll likely have to make some calls to verify the value of bank and investment accounts, Social Security survivor's benefits, and life insurance benefits. If you need help determining the nature and extent of any holdings, you will need to write to the decedent's bank and other financial institutions.

Consult an accountant or lawyer to determine the value of business assets and to create a plan to preserve them. If a business is a sole proprietorship, for example, you may need to understand what it takes to keep the business running and maintaining its value at the time of the owner's death.

If the decedent was part of a business partnership, your job will likely center on valuing the decedent's share. The partnership agreement may state what the partners must do if one of them dies—whether that is to dissolve the partnership, buy out the decedent's share, or continue the partnership with heirs retaining an interest. If there isn't an agreement in place, the onus is on the surviving partners to end the partnership and provide the executor with an accounting of the transaction and a payment for the decedent's portion of the business.

You may also need to get appraisals of real property. Appraising is not a one-size-fits-all profession. You might consult one appraiser to evaluate real estate, for example, and another to establish the value of art, antiques, jewelry, or collectibles. Chapter 23 gives guidance on how to find the appropriate professionals.

After you've established value, note how each asset was owned (see Chapter 12). This will help you determine how each asset will pass to an heir later. If you suspect the decedent had an asset you don't see documented, you can look to a number of organizations that may help you unearth assets ranging from retirement accounts to life insurance proceeds. Check sites including **www.missingmoney.com**, **www.unclaimed. org** and **www.policylocator.com**, and for help locating a lost pension, **www.dol.gov/ebsa** or **www.pensionhelp.org**. Each state in which the decedent lived may offer state-specific resources to recover lost assets as well.

Once you have taken inventory of assets, list liabilities, such as mortgages, loans, and credit card debts, along with when upcoming payments are due. Much of the debt record may have emerged when you collected critical documents. But running a credit report and contacting the decedent's financial institutions can help you fill out the picture and verify that you've taken an accurate survey. Don't forget to include recent expenses in the inventory such as funeral and medical expenses. Be prepared as well to hear from other creditors who have seen the death notice that is required by probate court in many states. State laws will specify how long creditors have to notify the estate after the notice's publication.

When you are finished, subtract liabilities from assets to determine the estate's net value. This is the money the estate has left to pay necessary taxes (see Chapter 20) and distribute to heirs.

*The Appendix includes a sample inventory and a sample letter for inquiries to financial institutions. Download blank templates of both documents as well as links to other information at **www.aier.org/bookstore**.*

12 • Decipher types of ownership

Knowing how each asset was owned will help you determine how it should pass to beneficiaries—and whether or not probate is necessary. Look for title documents or receipts as evidence of ownership.

Property owned *solely* in the name of the decedent does not have a formally designated beneficiary and will likely have to go through probate to pass to an heir. The exception is if you're settling a small estate, as defined by state law. In this case, there is a chance your state may let a certain amount of property pass to heirs either outside of probate or through a simplified probate process. Check your state's probate court website for more information.

If the person owned assets with *payable-on-death, transfer-on-death* or *in-trust-for* designations, which you might notice in bank and retirement accounts, life insurance policies, and trust documents, the assets will pass to the beneficiary without probate. In the case of payable-on-death or transfer-on-death accounts, the beneficiary will need to provide the financial institution with a certified copy of the decedent's death certificate. Assets held in trust are managed by the trustee, who notifies the beneficiary of his or her rights to the assets.

There are four different ways a person can own property with another person or group of people. If the decedent owned a home, automobile, investment account, or bank account in *joint tenancy with right of survivorship*, all owners have an equal right to an equal share of the asset. When one owner dies, the asset will pass directly to the surviving owners (not to the decedent's heirs). In this case, the asset will avoid probate. The portion of the asset that was owned by the decedent will potentially be subject to estate taxes (though if the only surviving owner is the spouse of the decedent, this will delay the tax until the spouse dies).

In many states, a person can own property through *tenancy by the entirety*, which is like joint tenancy with right of survivorship reserved for married couples and, in some states, registered domestic partners. This form of ownership gives both partners undivided rights to the property. It enables the entire property to pass directly to the surviving partner following the death of the first, avoiding probate and estate taxes.

If the decedent owned property with one or more people through *tenancy in common*, the percentage of the property he or she owned will pass to the chosen beneficiaries, without probate, rather than to the surviving owners. The value of the asset to the estate is the value of only the decedent's share, not the entire asset, and is taxed accordingly.

Nine states recognize *community property* in some form, which can exist between a husband and wife, and in a few states as of this writing, same-sex married couples and registered domestic partners as well. In these cases, the couple shares ownership of most assets and debts they accumulated together. If one spouse took out a home equity line of credit during the union, for example, his or her surviving spouse, rather than the estate as whole, is responsible for its repayment. Probate may not be needed to transfer community property to the surviving spouse, who also gets a tax benefit out of the arrangement. (Even though the surviving spouse owns just half of the community property asset, both that half and the decedent's half get a stepped-up tax basis based on its value at the date of death.) If you are settling an estate in a community property state, look to those state laws for specifics about how the assets pass to spouses.

On a separate but related note, if the decedent owned property outside of the United States, it will be subject to the tax laws in each country, and the estate risks having to pay a double tax on the property. In this case, consult an attorney or accountant familiar with international estates— you may also need an attorney or accountant in the country where the property is located—to minimize the estate's financial burden and clarify how the asset will pass to heirs. For more information about working with attorneys and other professionals, see Chapters 22 and 23.

13 • Probate defined

Probate is the legal process required to authorize a decedent's will, ensure creditors have an opportunity to make a claim on an estate, and appoint an executor to transfer estate assets to beneficiaries. If an estate includes assets that are held in trust, have a payable-on-death designation to a beneficiary, or are held jointly with someone else, these assets avoid probate. Other assets must pass through probate court in order to be distributed to heirs.

Avoiding probate is a common estate planning strategy for a few reasons. Probate can delay the settling of an estate, tying up property for a year or longer (lawsuits or contests to the will can prolong probate even further). It's also costly. Associated fees can amount to 5 percent or more of the estate's value. Finally, probate is public. Information about the debts, assets, and distributions that occur in probate court is available to anyone. As a result, there is the potential for heirs to become crime targets.

If the estate you're settling must pass through probate court, there is a chronology of steps you will have to take and paperwork you must file as part of the process. A checklist of likely probate court paperwork in the Appendix provides a general idea of the types of forms your court may need you to file.

Many states, for example, require you to publish a death notice in the newspaper as a formal announcement of the estate's probate. You will then need to notify specific creditors directly about the death. Typically, creditors must submit claims on an estate within three or four months of the announcement of probate.

Probate court will ask for an inventory and date-of-death valuation of estate assets and liabilities. The court will consult this inventory to ensure all estate property is available to be disbursed to beneficiaries. The court will then prioritize how the estate should pay any outstanding bills and estate expenses.

After the creditors' deadline for claim submission has expired and, as explained in later sections, you have paid debts and filed any necessary income and estate tax returns for the estate, you can distribute property to heirs.

It's important to know how and when you must communicate with the court, from start to finish. You'll likely have an easier time if you're settling an estate in one of the 17 states that has adopted some or all of the Uniform Probate Code—laws that were enacted to make the probate process simpler, particularly for small estates. Check with the Uniform Law Commission (go to **www.uniformlaws.org** and enter "uniform probate code" into the search box) for a map of states and territories that have adopted this code.

Your state's probate court website likely includes a self-help section that outlines the basics of the probate process. While some of these websites are more helpful (and comprehensible) than others, a scan of your state's site may help you know what questions to ask an attorney and how much of that attorney's counsel you want. You won't find everything on the state probate court's website, though, and probate clerks are legally restricted from providing legal advice or even guidance in filling out forms. That's why some people hire an attorney to handle the entire probate process. Even if you plan to manage most of the probate process yourself, consider consulting an estate attorney at certain points. The attorney can review all paperwork that you need to file with the court and explain legal terminology, for example, which could smooth your interactions with the probate judge who reviews the estate's file.

Still, if you want to go through probate without an attorney, you can— especially if you have the time and patience and a relatively uncomplicated estate. Several resources that can help you do this are listed in Chapter 25.

14 • How to manage a trust

Trusts are an attractive estate planning tool for good reason. Assets contained in a trust don't pass through probate, though some states may require you to file paperwork itemizing trust assets and pay the court a fee based on those values. When the grantor (the person who created the trust) passes away, the successor trustee gets immediate authority to manage the assets owned by the trust without having to wait for probate court's approval. This can be a great help if there are funeral bills that must be paid using estate funds, or if the estate includes complex assets, such as a family business, that need immediate attention.

In addition to helping avoid probate, trusts can protect an inheritance. They allow a grantor to leave funds to a beneficiary while putting rules around when, and for what purpose, the beneficiary can access the assets. For example, when a parent creates a trust for a child, a trustee is named to manage the assets until the child reaches a specific age, which can be older than 21. In addition, the trust provides a mechanism for the grantor to designate a specific use of funds, such as college tuition. Other more complex trusts can shield a large estate from estate tax while providing income for people or organizations the grantor chooses.

Executors are most likely to encounter two broad categories of trusts: irrevocable and revocable. These trusts can be living (*inter vivos*) trusts, which take effect once the grantor establishes the trust, or testamentary trusts, which are set up within a will and take effect at the grantor's death.

A grantor who creates an irrevocable trust agrees to give up control of the trust to the chosen trustee and beneficiary. As executor, you may be either or both of these things. The irrevocable trust can't be changed without the consent of the beneficiary, and the beneficiary does not yet control the assets. This removes the trust assets from the estate and makes them their own entity.

Irrevocable trusts tend to appeal to the wealthy because upon the grantor's death, any growth in trust assets will not be subject to federal estate tax. (The recipients of trust assets will still owe income tax when they receive income from the trust, however.) Irrevocable trusts are also shielded from creditor lawsuits, unlike revocable trusts.

A revocable living trust is a common tool many people use expressly to help their estate avoid probate, but it doesn't shield the estate from taxes. A revocable trust allows the grantor to retain control over the trust and the trust assets. Grantors can amend trusts, withdraw funds from them, or even dissolve them; they do not need agreement from either the successor trustee or beneficiary. Grantors can also use the trust to give heirs immediate authority over assets in case of emergencies such as health problems.

A trust doesn't take the place of a will; rather, the trust works alongside the will. Many trusts don't cover all of a decedent's assets, in which case you might find a *pour-over will* attached to the trust. This document covers assets that were meant for the trust but were never transferred. It can name children's guardians, if applicable, and ensure that all assets the grantor wanted to place in the trust end up there. If there was a pour-over will, the executor must transfer the assets mentioned in it to the trust. Because the assets weren't formally transferred before the death occurred, you may be required to go to probate court to implement the transfer.

If you are currently executor of an estate, the successor trustee (which may also be you) can access trust assets. The successor trustee operates in much the same way as the executor—following the language of the trust carefully, taking care of trust assets until they can be distributed, paying debts as needed, etc. If the estate contains a simple living trust with assets that can be disbursed in full soon after the death, there may already be a bank account tied to the trust. If you're the successor trustee, you have authority to take over that account.

In the case of a simple revocable living trust, the successor trustee will distribute assets to beneficiaries and then the trust will end—along with the successor trustee's job. (If you and your spouse created the trust together and you're the surviving spouse, you may well have inherited all trust assets and will keep the trust intact.)

If the trust is a more complicated one that will remain open for years, the successor trustee is responsible for filing a tax return (Form 1041) for the trust for every year it earns income of $600 or more. The executor, as opposed to the successor trustee, only needs to account for the trust in the final income tax return filed for the estate overall.

15 • Plans for minor children

If you're the executor of an estate that provides benefits to minor children, you're likely a close relative or friend and were entrusted to help with their care.

Instructions for guardianship should be stated in the will to ensure probate court can appoint the guardian(s) seamlessly following the death. If the will does not name a personal guardian, the court will choose someone who it deems will serve the best interests of the children. The executor, or concerned relatives or friends of the decedent, may provide input into the court's final decision. The guardian likely will need to update probate court regularly about funds received and spent on behalf of the children. If you are the executor but not also the guardian, your responsibilities end with the transfer of assets.

The minor children also will need a guardian to manage property they inherit. This responsibility can go to the personal guardian or someone else.

If the parent set up a trust to protect the children's inheritance and you are not the chosen trustee, your job is fairly simple: You transfer assets to the trust, if the will directs you to do so. In the more common case where you are both the executor and the successor trustee, your responsibilities will vary according to the terms of the trust.

A parent can leave gifts to minors outside the confines of a trust through the Uniform Transfers to Minors Act (UTMA). Nearly all states support the UTMA, which is a straightforward method for a person to leave any kind of property to a minor. It arranges for an adult custodian to manage the property until the minor reaches adulthood, as determined by the state. If the will has named you custodian, you are responsible for managing the assets for the minor according to the terms of the will. Alternatively, in many states when there is a fairly small amount of property involved, the executor can appoint a custodian of the children's property through the UTMA.

16 • If you're the sole beneficiary

Much of this book covers the challenges of settling an estate with multiple beneficiaries. If you're executor and sole beneficiary of the estate, your job will most likely be far easier. The transfer of assets is generally simpler, particularly if you are the surviving spouse and you and the decedent owned property jointly, or you are the sole beneficiary listed on life insurance and investment accounts.

If you are the surviving spouse, you may have a better handle of the decedent's assets and liabilities as well. And while you will still have to follow probate procedures if parts of the estate must pass through probate, you avoid the headaches that can accompany distributing assets to numerous beneficiaries.

17 • Invest and maintain assets

The general rule about investing estate assets is to be conservative. Particularly if you're holding assets that will be distributed to beneficiaries within several months, your goal should be to maintain assets for beneficiaries, not to make as much money as possible for the estate.

If the estate includes solely owned real estate and beneficiaries want to sell it, you are authorized to put it on the market once probate court has named you executor. If you're able to sell the property for more than what it was valued for as of the decedent's date of death, the estate will owe capital gains tax on the difference between the valuation at date of death and the sale price. As with liquid assets, you need to protect the value of real property until it is sold or distributed. You've probably already taken many of the basic steps mentioned in Chapter 5 to do so, including trimming the hedges and lawn, and making basic repairs. A real estate agent should be able to suggest people you can hire to maintain the property if you need help.

If the decedent left liquid investments that don't automatically pass to beneficiaries, review them with a professional following the death and at regular intervals thereafter. You may be able to keep investments in place if the decedent took minimal risks. If the estate includes some volatile stocks, diversify the investments by selling them and then transferring any proceeds into the estate bank account or some other conservative investment. If the assets plummet in value as a result of risks you took, beneficiaries can hold you responsible. Whatever you do, don't forget to keep careful records of what steps you've taken to protect the estate.

If you're the successor trustee of the decedent's trust, you have immediate authority following the death to invest and sell assets held in the trust. How conservatively you invest these assets depends on the age and risk tolerance of the beneficiaries. A more aggressively invested portfolio to be liquidated many years into the future might better tolerate market fluctuations. Again here, a professional can help you set the investment allocations appropriate for the trust's time horizon. As always, keep careful records.

18 • Meet estate expenses

During the period you're managing the estate, you may need income to maintain a property or pay legal fees and taxes. In those cases you will need to decide which estate assets to sell for these uses. The will may give you direction about how soon to sell which assets. If not, here are a few guidelines:

If there aren't sufficient liquid assets to pay estate expenses but there are non-liquid assets on hand, you may have to sell some non-liquid assets to cover estate costs. Weigh the tax liability of selling each of these assets and get input from beneficiaries. Determining the tax liability may require consulting a certified public accountant (CPA) or other tax professional. You may find such a consultation helpful in demonstrating that you have beneficiaries' best interests in mind when determining what to sell.

In general, assets can be used to settle the estate and pay off debts and taxes, but not to cover costs that are peripheral to the administration of the estate (a court could scrutinize your expenses for meals and travel, for example). If other beneficiaries would object to how you're spending the funds, reconsider the expense—or at least document it and be prepared to defend it.

19 • Pay debts

When you took inventory of the decedent's assets, you likely found bills or other documents indicating debt. Unless the decedent co-owned assets and debt with a family member, the decedent's relatives typically are not responsible for paying off estate debt with their own money, and the estate may not even be legally required to pay all debts. (If you paid any costs associated with estate administration before you were formally named executor, you can reimburse yourself. Just keep your receipts handy.)

Before you pay any debts, first ensure that you have taken a full inventory of the decedent's assets and validate each debt. This can make you aware of the total funds available for debt payment and any contracts that cancel debts owed. (Some insurance policies, for example, offer the benefit of canceling debt upon a variety of events, including death.) If the estate has more debts than assets, look to your probate court, if applicable, or your state's laws, which rank creditors in order of priority for you. Since you may not need to pay off certain debts in full (or in some cases at all), determine which expenses are most important before writing any checks. If more informal claims to the estate arise—if, for example, the decedent had verbally agreed to pay, with remaining funds from his estate, a relative who provided care—solicit beneficiaries' opinions to determine your next steps.

Be aware of tasks that have a deadline and those that don't. While you need to file the will with probate court within a set timeframe in order to pay debts, you don't need to rush to pay bills as they come in. In fact, you may have to wait until probate court prioritizes creditors' claims for the decedent.

You will likely pay debts using the estate bank account you set up after the death—or in the case of a simple living trust, the bank account tied to the trust. If the estate includes a more complicated trust, like for example, a child's trust designed to secure assets for many years into the future, there may be an account in place that consolidates cash and investments. You can take over this account as successor trustee. If this sort of account does not exist, you may find it helpful to set one up to manage beneficiaries' expenses and investment balances in one place.

20 • File tax returns

More than likely, you will have to file a few tax returns on behalf of the decedent and the estate overall. State and federal income tax returns for the last year of the decedent's life are common, as well as state and federal income tax returns for the estate.

The same filing guidelines generally apply to deceased and living individual taxpayers. Unless the decedent received little or no income in the last months of life, you'll have to file Form 1040 on the April 15 after the death. (Check **www.irs.gov** for the latest income thresholds.) Once you complete this return, write "deceased" at the top, along with the decedent's name and date of death.

The tax return you must file on behalf of the estate (Form 1041) covers income received after the death—for example, income earned on solely owned bank and investment accounts, or proceeds from the sale of the decedent's solely owned home. If the estate contains assets that pass outside of probate to beneficiaries or co-owners, the heirs are responsible for filing any required tax returns.

Chances are good the estate you're settling does not owe federal estate tax (Form 706). The thresholds change often, but as of 2014, only estates worth more than $5.34 million must file a federal estate tax return. And if the estate is passing to a surviving spouse or to a tax-exempt charity, no estate tax is owed regardless of the size of the estate.

When assessing the value of an estate likely to owe federal estate taxes, you can use a date-of-death valuation or a valuation taken six months later (if the asset has not already been distributed within those six months). If the estate contains securities or real estate that are likely to change significantly in value during that time, you'll naturally want to select the valuation date that will result in a lower total estate value. You'll have to choose your preferred date within one year after the estate's federal estate tax return is due.

Depending on your state, the estate may still have to file a state estate tax return even if no federal estate tax is owed. Fewer than half of the states collect estate taxes, but those that do tend to have lower thresholds than the federal threshold. (New Jersey's, for example, is the lowest at $675,000.) For 2014, state estate tax rates ranged from 9.5 percent to 20 percent across the states. But the estate may owe only minimal state estate tax (or none at all) if eligible deductions bring the total value of the estate below the state threshold.

It is less likely, though certainly possible, that you'll have additional returns to file. If you are also the successor trustee, for example, you may have to file state and federal income tax returns for a trust that has earned a certain amount of income determined by the state. There could also be inheritance tax owed. (Note: While the terms "estate tax" and "inheritance tax" are sometimes used interchangeably, estate tax is the tax the estate owes; inheritance tax is the tax owed by the heir upon receipt of the inheritance. Some states collect one or both of these taxes.)

21 • Disburse property

Estate assets pass to heirs according to how each asset was owned. Assets held in ways that avoid probate—such as a life insurance policy, a payable-on-death bank account, or a living trust—can pass to heirs almost immediately after a death. As the executor, you will have to transfer other inherited property and funds to the heirs.

Assets that must go through probate can only transfer to heirs after you have determined the estate has sufficient assets to cover legal and court fees, taxes, and debts, and the deadline has passed for creditors to claim any assets through probate.

Make sure you have sufficient assets in the estate to pay debts and taxes before you pass assets to the beneficiaries. Even if a beneficiary pushes for early payment, you must wait. If the estate has insufficient assets due to your actions, you risk having to pay the debts and taxes from your personal funds.

Even people with detailed estate plans may still leave a number of tangible assets without specific heirs. Once you have a reasonable idea of each item's fair market value, you'll need a plan to distribute the property to new owners. Some executors have found it worthwhile to stage a mock auction in which each heir is assigned a pool of credits to "purchase" items from the estate. Other executors have given heirs colored tags to post on items they would like to own. Both of these strategies can be adapted when heirs live far apart. If multiple heirs want an item, the executor can help them negotiate a peaceful resolution.

You'll likely have items left over that no one wants to claim. An estate liquidator can clear these items, or you can donate them to charities and receive a tax deduction to offset taxes owed. Once all taxes and debts are paid, all the property is disbursed, and, if applicable, probate court has approved the settlement of the estate, your obligations as executor have been fulfilled.

22 • Consulting an attorney

As you move through the steps of settling an estate, you may decide to hire an attorney to provide occasional counsel or to manage the entire process, or you may decide to not hire an attorney at all. Most likely, you will depend on an attorney to help you navigate the legal and tax implications of the estate and to provide guidance at least periodically.

It can be tempting to rely on a well-meaning relative or friend for advice, hire an attorney on the low end of the fee spectrum, or, if the estate avoids probate, hire no legal counsel. However, unless you're well versed in the law, the estate is small, or most assets will avoid probate, consult an attorney who specializes in estate planning because the law changes so regularly.

As you progress through the stages of settling an estate, there are several tasks you may decide to handle yourself. Filing the will with probate often can be done easily, as can getting a tax ID number for the estate and setting up an estate checking account. Other tasks that are comparatively simple are notifying beneficiaries named in the will and notifying creditors of the probate case (if it's a small estate with few major claims expected). Another job that can be easily done without legal advice is finalizing an itemized list of estate assets and debts for the probate court.

An attorney can be invaluable in outlining probate tasks and paperwork specific to the decedent's state if the estate will pass through probate court. (If you miss a key probate court deadline or blatantly ignore procedures, the court can remove you as executor, charge you a fine, or, in extreme cases, sentence you to prison.)

Your attorney can manage all of the tasks required by probate court. Or, in a more limited capacity, your attorney can coach you through them by accompanying you to meetings with the probate judge, if applicable, or by answering legal or tax-related questions. An attorney can also point you to other specialists you may need.

Legal expertise can be especially useful if you need to notify people who may complicate the settling of the estate. An attorney can communicate with people who would traditionally inherit from the estate but are not mentioned in the will and may challenge it, for example. If a business partnership is involved, an attorney can help with any necessary transfer of ownership. Or, if the estate is large or involves a bankruptcy, an attorney can notify creditors looking to collect payment. Finally, an attorney with international experience or even one based in another country may be necessary if an estate has overseas holdings.

If you decide to consult an attorney, do some legwork in advance to make the most of the person's time and save on fees. It will help if you have a complete estate inventory to start, and if you can readily provide the will and/or trust. Other helpful facts include the names of surviving family members, information on the decedent's previous marriages (if applicable) and how they ended, and details about disputes between heirs or business partners that could pose a challenge.

You're typically under no obligation to hire the attorney who created the estate plan or drafted the will, so work with the person who makes you most comfortable. Meet with a few contenders and get a written statement from each person about the expected fees and fee structure. Ask specific questions as you interview attorneys: How much experience do you have in settling estates? Are you willing to work with me if I'd like to handle much of the probate process myself? Can you provide an overview of what steps I'll need to take and when they need to be taken? Do you charge a flat fee, a percentage of the size of the estate (avoid this arrangement), or an hourly fee? Get an itemized list of potential costs. If you can't get that kind of transparency, keep looking for an attorney who can provide that. And remember, once you've hired the attorney, you can keep consultation costs down by reserving several questions for a single meeting or phone call instead of making many one-off phone calls.

23 • Consulting accountants and other professionals

An accountant can be an important resource too, especially if the estate is large enough to owe federal and state estate tax, or the decedent operated a business and you need to supply an appraiser with information to help determine its value. The decedent's regular accountant likely has helpful background knowledge of the estate's finances and can provide tax strategies that may help preserve the heirs' assets. The accountant can also prepare and file income and estate tax returns on the estate's behalf.

Depending on the size of the estate and how long it will take to settle it, you may need counsel from other professionals. For example, a financial adviser can prepare an investment plan if you'll be managing the estate's assets over a long period. An insurance agent can help you assess whether you need to insure estate assets and can distribute life insurance proceeds to beneficiaries.

If the decedent did not have an accountant or financial adviser and you don't currently consult these professionals yourself, the decedent's bank or the estate's attorney can be a helpful source of contacts. As you would do when hiring an attorney, interview several candidates, ask about each specialist's fee structure and experience in managing cases like yours, and make sure communication between you is clear.

Appraisers of various specialties can value business interests, real estate and personal belongings in preparation for either sale or equitable distribution to heirs. Look to the American Society of Appraisers (**www.appraisers.org**) to find an experienced appraiser. Specific to real estate, the Appraisal Institute (**www.appraisalinstitute.org**) is another helpful resource.

Real estate agents can market property for sale and also connect you with an estate liquidator to help you sell, donate, or dispose of remaining property. If you're unfamiliar with real estate agents in the region, **www. realtor.com** provides a searchable database that includes detailed profiles and information on each agent's current listings. Interview three prospective agents and get their market assessments of the decedent's property prior to listing it for sale.

24 • What this will cost

The cost of settling an estate can vary widely—from several hundreds of dollars to tens of thousands and higher. The cost will depend on several factors, chief among these is the complexity of the estate and how the assets will pass to heirs. Another possibly significant contributor to the cost of settling the estate is whether the estate will owe federal and state estate taxes. Remember, only estates valued above $5.34 million (according to 2014 laws) must file a federal estate tax return. And, for these large estates, no filing is required if the estate is transferred to a spouse or tax-exempt charity. Contests to the will, the amount of help you get from your probate court, and the amount of help you need from professionals can also affect your settlement costs.

It's easy to rack up steep expenses. For example, attorney fees can easily reach $200 to $300 per hour. Even if you hire someone for a flat fee, there may be additional expenses if the estate requires more than basic services. An hourly fee of $100 to $250 is common for certified public accountants and professional appraisers, though appraisers' fees can range more widely depending on geographical location.

The general rule of thumb is to estimate total costs at approximately 5 percent of the estate's value, exclusive of taxes. That includes fees for the probate court, if applicable, and hiring an attorney, accountant, or appraiser. Costs for estates that don't go to probate can be lower.

25 • Where to get more help

The following books and websites were helpful during the research of this book and could be useful additional resources to you as you settle an estate.

BOOKS

The Executor's Guide: Settling a Loved One's Estate or Trust, Mary Randolph. Nolo, 2012. Using examples, illustrations and plain terms, this book—one of the most accessible ones available—coaches you through the estate settlement process step-by-step, with an overview of probate, tips on hiring professionals, and state-specific information.

The Executor's Handbook, Theodore Hughes and David Klein. Skyhorse Publishing, 2013. This guide provides an overview of the estate settlement process that can help you educate yourself before consulting estate professionals.

How to Avoid Financial Tangles, AIER Research Staff, American Institute for Economic Research, 2009. By giving general advice on a variety of topics, this book helps people understand and manage many basic financial tasks.

How to Invest Wisely: Managing Assets for the Long Term, Larry Pratt, American Institute for Economic Research, 2010. A guide for investors, this book outlines a low-cost, low-risk approach to building and holding a portfolio.

How to Settle an Estate: A Manual for Executors and Trustees, Charles K. Plotnick and Stephan R. Leimberg. Penguin Group, 2002. This introduction to serving as an executor helps you organize yourself, navigate taxes, and hire an estate settlement team.

If Something Should Happen (revision), Marla Brill, Jennifer Keeney-Bleeg, and Marcia Stamell, American Institute for Economic Research, 2015.

An organizer and primer that brings key financial, legal, and personal information into one place.

WEBSITES

www.avvo.com: If legal questions arise as you begin managing the estate, you can post them for free on this site and wait for attorneys to respond—often within a couple of hours. While the site is no substitute for legal counsel, it can help you educate yourself about the settlement process.

www.law.freeadvice.com: Find a step-by-step guide to the typical probate process, as well as other baseline information about various parts of the law.

www.nolo.com: Find accessible articles about many areas of the law, do-it-yourself tools and an attorney directory.

www.rocketlawyer.com: For a modest monthly fee, get step-by-step guidance on how to create estate planning documents and executor's correspondence, and ask an attorney for legal advice or a review of legal documents.

www.findlaw.com: Browse FAQs, checklists and forums about estate planning and administration, among other areas of the law.

www.statelocalgov.net: Access this directory of state and local government websites for information about your probate court and state laws.

If you sense the decedent had an asset you don't see documented, you can look to a number of organizations that may help you unearth assets ranging from life insurance proceeds to retirement accounts. Check sites including **www.missingmoney.com**, **www.unclaimed.org** and **www.policylocator.com**, and for help locating a lost pension, **www.dol.gov/ebsa or www.pensionhelp.org**.

Unless the decedent received little or no income in the last months of life, you'll have to file Form 1040 on the April 15 after the death. Check **www.irs.gov** for the latest income thresholds.

www.extension.umn.edu/family/personal-finance/who-gets-grandmas-yellow-pie-plate: Find tips for distributing property to heirs thoughtfully and with minimal conflict.

Appendix

ELEMENTS OF AN ESTATE PLAN

If you have the opportunity to discuss the estate plan with the person who has selected you as executor, you can help avoid conflict with beneficiaries and ensure you're settling the estate in accordance with the person's wishes. Consider these elements together:

Take inventory of assets. Make lists of both tangible assets (e.g., real estate, furniture, jewelry, electronics, vehicles and other items of value) and intangible assets (e.g., IRAs, bank accounts and life insurance).

Take inventory of debts. List mortgages, lines of credit, credit cards and any other debt owed. Run a credit report to take stock of existing credit card accounts.

Confirm beneficiary/transfer-on-death designatioCheck life insurance policies, annuities, and IRA and 401(k) accounts to ensure that chosen beneficiaries are listed correctly. Confirm the payable-on-death designation on bank accounts (or select this option to help the account avoid probate later).

Talk to an estate planner. A financial planner or an estate attorney with financial planning expertise can help create a strategy for protecting assets now and providing for beneficiaries later. Topics for discussion may include trusts, estate taxes, guardianship of minors, succession of a business, charitable giving, and power-of-attorney for end-of-life financial and health matters.

Create/update the will. This will ensure assets are distributed according to the decedent's wishes. Update the will after any life events (e.g., marriages, divorces, births or deaths) that could change who will inherit.

Discuss plans with heirs. Prevent misunderstandings later.

Record any changes to the above information. Keep files current.

Retain copies of all legal documents. This will help prevent delays as you begin your duties as executor.

EXECUTOR'S CHECKLIST: KEY RESPONSIBILITIES

- [ ] Find and review the will.
- [ ] Obtain copies of the death certificate. The funeral director or county vital records office can help.
- [ ] Decide when, and to what extent, you will consult an attorney.
- [ ] Submit the will to probate court. (Do this regardless of whether estate will pass to heirs through probate.)
- [ ] Have probate court confirm your appointment as executor. The court will issue you Letters Testamentary.
- [ ] Provide a notice of death to credit card companies, banks and any organizations that had been providing benefits to the decedent.
- [ ] Apply for a tax identification number with the IRS.
- [ ] Open a bank account for the estate.
- [ ] Gather the names, Social Security numbers and contact information of heirs.
- [ ] Gather the personal papers, financial records and tax returns of the decedent.
- [ ] Take inventory of estate assets and liabilities.
- [ ] Contact the decedent's life insurer and former employer, if applicable, to ensure outstanding benefits are paid to the estate or beneficiaries.
- [ ] Determine the value of estate assets with help from accountants and appraisers as needed.
- [ ] Determine which assets, if any, will need to pass to heirs through probate court. File documents to open a probate case if needed.
- [ ] Manage assets. Take care of decedent's real estate and personal property and determine which assets may need to be invested or sold.
- [ ] Pay estate debts and expenses using estate account.
- [ ] Pay taxes on behalf of the decedent and the estate.
- [ ] Disburse estate property to heirs.
- [ ] Close the estate account once you have paid expenses and taxes, and all estate property has been distributed.
- [ ] Close the estate case with probate court, if applicable.

PROBATE COURT PAPERWORK

Potentially, there are dozens of forms you will need to file with probate court and—surprise—they vary from state to state. But here is a sampling of some you may see. For more guidance, you can consult your probate court's staff, website, or self-help guide (many courts publish them or post them online). Several self-help publications, such as *The Executor's Guide* and **www.law.freeadvice.com**, can help you identify the overall structure of the probate process and consider questions to ask an attorney familiar with probate proceedings, should you decide to use one.

Publication Notice

Bond

Petition for Formal Probate of Will

Inventory

Creditor's Claim

Affidavit of Domicile

Affidavit of Witness to Will

Small Estate Affidavit

Petition for Appointment of Special Personal Representative

Petition for Supervised Administration

Sale of Real Estate

Statement of Confirmation of Testamentary Trustee (in some states)

General Trust Petition (in some states)

Petition for Appointment of Guardian

INVENTORY WORKSHEET

The sample inventory on the following pages itemizes a hypothetical decedent's assets and liabilities to show how distribution of assets can vary based on how they are owned. The basic types of ownership are defined in Chapter 12. For a blank template you can download, go to **www.aier.org/bookstore**.

ASSETS				
Asset type	Account number	Date-of-death value of decedent's share	How asset was owned	Probate required
BANK ACCOUNTS Savings account, New York Bank & Trust	1234	$25,437	Solely	Yes
Checking account, New York Bank & Trust	234-6789	$3,211	Joint tenancy with Mary Mason	No
BUSINESS INTERESTS Mason Auto Repair		$300,000	Tenancy in common, Beneficiary John Mason	No
LIFE INSURANCE Prudential policy, Beneficiary Mary Mason	97344-1	$500,000	Solely	No
Personal property		$36,500	Solely	Yes
Antiques		$17,600		
Artwork		$5,400		
Real estate		$250,000	Solely	Yes
RETIREMENT ACCOUNTS IRA at American Funds, Beneficiary Mary Mason	345-78965	$31,650	Solely	No
401(K) at Hartford Financial Services Group, Beneficiary Mary Mason	178-9087	$65,824	Solely	No

SECURITIES American Funds mutual funds, Beneficiary Mary Mason	457-9876	$100,516	Solely	No
VEHICLES 2010 Honda Accord		$12,700	Solely	Yes
TOTAL ASSETS		**$1,348,838**		

LIABILITIES			
Liability type	Total owed	Account number	Next payment amount, Due date
Business loan, New York Bank & Trust	$10,500	347890	$350.25 Dec. 5, 2014
Car loan, American Honda Service Co.	$950	7908654	$233.46 Dec. 15, 2014
CREDIT CARD Citibank MasterCard Chase Visa	 $3,502 $653	 34567890 78906543	$3502 (or min. $140) Nov. 25, 2014 $653 (or min. $26) Dec.10, 2014
Funeral expenses	$10,105		$10,105 Nov. 30, 2014
Medical expenses	$5,187		$5,187 Dec. 10, 2014
Mortgage, Chase	$4,600	4557890	$1,151 Dec. 5, 2014
TOTAL LIABILITIES	**$35,497**		

Net estate value: $1,313,341

BENEFICIARIES				
Name	Mailing Address	Email Address	Phone Number	Social Security Number

SAMPLE LETTER

Following the death of the decedent, you will need to notify various parties of the death so you can put together an accurate inventory of the estate's assets and liabilities. You can use the sample letter on the next page as a model to help you gather information. Download a template of this letter at **www.aier.org/bookstore.** You can also visit **www.rocketlawyer. com** to build your own correspondence.

Boston Private Bank & Trust Company
One Cambridge Center
Cambridge, MA 02142

Re: Estate of Robert J. Barry, account number 456-279
Dear Sir or Madam,

I am the executor of the estate of Robert J. Barry, who died on April 24, 2014. See the enclosed certificate from Boston Probate & Family Court as evidence of my appointment as executor.

It is my understanding that Mr. Barry held checking account No. 456-279 with your institution. Please send me written confirmation that this is correct, along with written confirmation of any additional accounts Mr. Barry held with you, including but not limited to personal checking accounts, retirement accounts, business accounts and loans, regardless of whether these accounts were owned solely by Mr. Barry or jointly with others. For each account, I am hoping you can confirm 1) the account number; 2) the date-of-death balance and the accrued, but unpaid, interest; and 3) if there were joint owners.

Would you also let me know if Mr. Barry kept a safe deposit box with your institution?

I have enclosed a self-addressed, stamped envelope for your convenience. If you have questions, please contact me at 508-555-3456.

Thank you very much for your assistance with this request.

Best regards,

Carole Barry
Executor of the estate of Robert J. Barry

Index